STAR CAT

BOOK 01

BY JAMES TURNER

Star Cat: Book 1
is a
DAVID FICKLING BOOK

First published in Great Britain in 2014 by
David Fickling Books,
31 Beaumont Street,
Oxford, OX1 2NP

www.davidficklingbooks.com

Text and Illustrations © James Turner, 2014

978-1-910200-06-3

1 3 5 7 9 10 8 6 4 2

David Fickling Books supports the Forest Stewardship Council (FSC®),
the leading international forest certification organisation. All our titles
that are printed on Greenpeace-approved FSC®-certified paper carry the FSC® logo.

MIX
Paper from
responsible sources
FSC® C015140

DAVID FICKLING BOOKS Reg. No. 8340307

A CIP catalogue record for this book is available from the British Library

Printed and bound in Great Britain by Polestar Stones.

SPACE TABLE OF SPACE CONTENTS

SPECIAL SPACE THANKS TO
JOE MORGAN AND REBECCA BURGESS

WELCOME ABOARD THE STAR CAT

CAPTAIN SPACEINGTON

COMMANDER OF THE HALF CAT, HALF SPACESHIP STAR CAT, CAPTAIN SPACEINGTON DREAMS OF BEING THE BRAVEST CAPTAIN IN THE FLEET, BUT SOMEHOW WHENEVER A MISSION COMES ALONG THINGS NEVER QUITE GO TO PLAN...

SCIENCE OFFICER PLIXX

WHAT PLIXX LACKS IN SCIENTIFIC KNOWLEDGE SHE MORE THAN MAKES UP FOR WITH ENTHUSIASM. SHE MAY NOT KNOW THE DIFFERENCE BETWEEN A PROTON AND A NEUTRON, BUT SHE'S ALWAYS HAPPY TO WHACK THEM BOTH WITH A HAMMER AND HOPE FOR THE BEST.

KEY:
1. BRIDGE
2. AIRLOCK / HAIRBALL MANUFACTURE AREA
3. FUEL TANK
4. SCIENCE BAY
5. CREW QUARTERS
6. BRIG

KEY:
7. EXTERNAL AURAL RECEPTOR (E.A.R.)
8. SUPER COMPUTER
9. SHOCK ABSORBER
10. SPACE MOUSE DETECTOR

THE PILOT

DIPDPMBUF CJTDVJUT TQSFBE XJUI LFUDIVQ. DMJNC VQ B MBEES BOE KVNQ JOUP B TXJNNJOH QPPM GJMMFE XJUI KBN. NZ USPVTFST IBWF UVSOFE JOUP B QVSQMF HJSBGGF. J IBWF TFFO UIF GVUVSF BOE JU JT KVTU B SFBMMZ CJH PXM.

ROBOT ONE

ROBOT ONE IS THE MOST ADVANCED ROBOT EVER CREATED, WITH A COMPUTER MIND TEN MILLION TIMES MORE POWERFUL THAN THE SQUISHY BLOB OF GREY GOO WE CALL A BRAIN. (OR AT LEAST THAT'S WHAT HE LIKES TO TELL EVERYONE AT EVERY POSSIBLE OPPORTUNITY.)

THE DEEPEST REACHES OF SPACE...

FILLED WITH MYSTERY, DANGER AND ALIEN HORRORS...

AND ALSO A BUNCH OF STARS AND MOONS AND STUFF LIKE THAT...

ONLY ONE VESSEL DARES TO TRAVERSE THIS INFINITE VOID...

STAR CAT

HALF CAT, HALF SPACESHIP, IT IS THE STAR CAT'S ONGOING MISSION TO EXPLORE THE MYSTERIES OF THE UNIVERSE...

AND ONBOARD THE STAR CAT WE FIND THE ONLY SPACE-FARER COURAGEOUS ENOUGH TO COMMAND THIS CRAFT...

CAPTAIN SPACEINGTON!

GRAB!

NEOWW! PYEW! PYEW! CAPTAIN SPACEINGTON SAVES THE UNIVERSE AGAIN! EVERYONE CHEERS AND GIVES HIM MEDALS AND ICE CREAM!

CAPTAIN SPACEINGTON!

SCIENCE OFFICER PLIXX! DON'T YOU EVER KNOCK?? I AM WORKING ON IMPORTANT CAPTAIN'S BUSINESS!

SHWOONK

SORRY SIR, BUT THERE'S AN INCOMING COMMUNICATION FOR YOU FROM THE SPACE MAYOR HIMSELF!

ALSO MY HANDS ARE TOO SQUIDGEY TO KNOCK WITH.

THE SPACE MAYOR? QUICKLY! TO THE BRIDGE!

ON THE BRIDGE...

CAPTAIN SPACEINGTON! I HAVE AN URGENT MISSION FOR YOU!

INCOMING COMMUNICATION: SPACE MAYOR

OOH! A MISSION! WHAT IS IT, SIR?

NOTORIOUS SPACE CRIMINAL, DARK RECTANGLE HAS JUST ESCAPED FROM SPACE PRISON! WE SUSPECT THAT HE PLANS TO ROB THE SPACE BANK NEAR TO YOUR CURRENT LOCATION.

DARK RECTANGLE 21337

HE MUST BE STOPPED BEFORE HE COMMITS THIS HEINOUS SPACE CRIME!

YOU CAN COUNT ON US, SPACE MAYOR! WE'LL HAVE THIS FOUR-CORNERED FIEND IN CUSTODY BEFORE YOU CAN SAY 'IRREGULAR QUADRILATERAL'!

SALUTE!

INCOMING C SPACE M

GOOD LUCK CAPTAIN, WE'RE ALL COUNTING ON YOU.

PILOT, HOW LONG UNTIL WE REACH THE SPACE BANK?

J MJLF FHHT UP CF TDSBNCMFE.

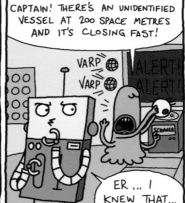

THE **BIG LET DOWN**

THE LEGENDARY LOST PLANET INFLATIA. NO ONE HAS SET FOOT ON THIS MYSTERIOUS WORLD IN A THOUSAND YEARS...

BUT WHAT'S THIS? ON THE SURFACE ARE THAT MASTER OF POLYGONAL PERIL, DARK RECTANGLE, AND HIS LOYAL HENCHSHAPE, MURKY HEXAGON! WHAT VILLAINOUS SCHEME IS AFOOT?

AT LAST, WE'VE FOUND IT!

OOH!

THE GREAT GALACTIC STOPPER!

UM, VERY IMPRESSIVE, OH PERPENDICULAR POTENTATE, BUT, UM, WHAT DOES IT DO?

IT'S THIS STOPPER THAT KEEPS ALL THE AIR IN THE GALAXIES... AND WHEN I PULL IT OUT I WILL DEFLATE THE UNIVERSE! WUHAHAHA!

LUCKILY A TEAM OF HEROES IS HERE TO SAVE US, THE CREW OF THE ...

STAR CAT

ON BOARD, THE CREW IS ALWAYS ALERT AND READY FOR ACTION...

UGH, MY BOREDOM PROCESSOR IS RUNNING AT 100% CAPACITY.

CAPTAIN SPACEINGTON! EMERGENCY! EMERGENCY!

GREAT GALAXIES! WHAT IS IT, PLIXX? METEOR STORM? SPACE OCTOPUS? HOT-DOG PIRATES?

WORSE THAN THAT, SIR! OUR SUPPLY OF STRAWBERRY ICE CREAM HAS ALMOST RUN OUT!

DANGER VERY LOW

I HARDLY THINK THAT COUNTS AS AN EMERGENCY, PLIXX.

OH, AND WE ONLY HAVE ONE PORTION OF CHOCOLATE-CHIP ICE CREAM LEFT.

WHY DIDN'T YOU SAY SO! SET A COURSE FOR THE ICE CREAM PLANET AT ONCE!

PAH! WE ROBOTS HAVE NO NEED OF YOUR PUNY BIOLOGICAL "FOOD". WE SCOFF AT YOUR FEEBLE ORGANIC "ICE CREAM" AND CHORTLE DERISIVELY AT YOUR PRIMITIVE HUMAN "FIZZY CHEWS".

THIS MISSION IS OF NO ...EST ... ME!

BUT ROBOT ONE, YOU'RE EATING ICE CREAM RIGHT NOW.

BUT THIS IS MINT CHOC SWIRL. THAT DOESN'T COUNT!

PILOT, ACTIVATE HYPER WARP, LEVEL 5!

SBEJTIFT.

PULL!

OPEN!

EMERGE...

5 MINUTES LATER...

HERE WE ARE, CREW, PLANET ICE CREAM!

JUST IN TIME, TOO, THE ONLY ICE CREAM WE HAVE LEFT IS BAKED BEAN FLAVOUR...

OOH, MY FAVOURITE!

PILOT, TAKE US DOWN.

LAND!

SHOONK

WELCOME TO THE ICE CREAM PLANET WHERE YOUR EVERY ICE CREAM-RELATED DREAM CAN COME TRUE!

UM, IT'S A BIT MORE, ER... RUBBERY THAN I EXPECTED...

HMM

ROBOT ONE, ARE YOU SURE YOU GOT THE DIRECTIONS RIGHT?

OF COURSE! MY DIRECTIONAL ALGORITHM IS ACCURATE TO WITHIN 1000TH OF A MILLIMETRE!

AND ANYWAY, I USED THIS MAP AND THE ICE CREAM PLANET IS RIGHT HERE.

HMM.

MY FIRST MAP OF SPACE

TAP TAP

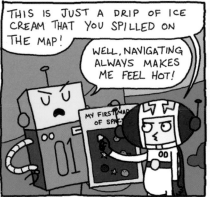

THIS IS JUST A DRIP OF ICE CREAM THAT YOU SPILLED ON THE MAP!

WELL, NAVIGATING ALWAYS MAKES ME FEEL HOT!

MY FIRST MAP OF SPACE

WELL, MAYBE THIS IS THE RIGHT PLACE ANYWAY. LOOK, THERE'S SOMEONE, LET'S ASK THEM!

NO SHOES

YOO HOO! DO YOU H... ANY BUTTERSCOTCH RIPPLE?

I'M AFRAID THERE'S ONLY ONE FLAVOUR YOU'LL BE HAVING TODAY...

THREE SCOOPS OF DOUBLE-CHOCOLATE DOOM! HA HA HA HA!

WITH MISERY SYRUP!

GASP!

DARK RECTANGLE!

CAN I HAVE SPRINKLES ON THAT?

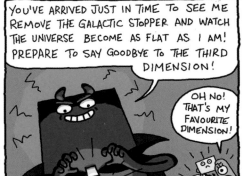

YOU'VE ARRIVED JUST IN TIME TO SEE ME REMOVE THE GALACTIC STOPPER AND WATCH THE UNIVERSE BECOME AS FLAT AS I AM! PREPARE TO SAY GOODBYE TO THE THIRD DIMENSION!

OH NO! THAT'S MY FAVOURITE DIMENSION!

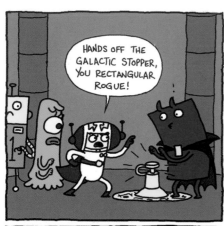

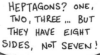

ANOTHER VILLAINOUS PLOT TO DESTROY THE UNIVERSE FOILED. ALL IN A DAY'S WORK FOR THE CREW OF THE ... STAR CAT

I HOPE YOU WIPED YOUR FEET.

PEW! PEW! DID YOU SEE HOW THE CAPTAIN DID THAT? SO COOL!

UM, I'M NOT SURE YOU SHOULD BE PLAYING WITH THAT, PLIXX...

I THINK YOU'VE JUST OVERLOADED MY BAD IDEA SENSOR...

WAGGLE

BEEP BEEP BEEP BEEP BEEP

OH, YOU'RE NO FUN, ROBOT ONE, IT'S NOT LIKE I'M GOING TO DO SOMETHING SILLY, LIKE ACCIDENTALLY SHOOT OUT THE GALACTIC STOPPER OR ANYTHING!

OOPS

DISCOMBOBULATE!

ZOP!

CALAMITOUS COMETS! YOU'VE DESTROYED THE GALACTIC STOPPER! THE UNIVERSE IS GOING TO DEFLATE LIKE A BADLY MADE SOUFFLÉ!

PFFFFFT!

IS THAT BAD?

WE'VE ONLY GOT A FEW SECONDS BEFORE THE UNIVERSE IS AS FLAT AS A SPACE PANCAKE!

I FEEL LIKE I'VE LET YOU ALL DOWN...

DE FL AT E!

THIS IS TERRIBLE! I LOOK SO HANDSOME IN THREE DIMENSIONS!

SOMEBODY DO SOMETHING!

UM

WHAT'S THE PILOT DOING?

LIFT!

CSJFGDBTFT.

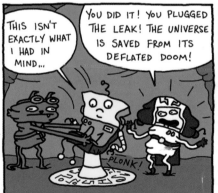

THIS ISN'T EXACTLY WHAT I HAD IN MIND...

YOU DID IT! YOU PLUGGED THE LEAK! THE UNIVERSE IS SAVED FROM ITS DEFLATED DOOM!

PLONK!

BUT, CAPTAIN, WE'RE STILL ALL FLOPPY! EVERY TIME I TRY TO EAT MY JELLY MY SPOON JUST FOLDS OVER!

YOU'RE RIGHT, PLIXX, WE NEED TO REINFLATE THE UNIVERSE ... BUT THE AMOUNT OF GAS REQUIRED WOULD BE ASTRONOMICAL!

BLORP

BUT SUDDENLY!

STARTLING STARS! THE UNIVERSE REINFLATED! BUT WHAT COULD POSSIBLY PRODUCE SUCH AN INCREDIBLE VOLUME OF GAS ??

FLOMP!

UM, SORRY, THAT ALWAYS HAPPENS WHEN I EAT BAKED-BEAN ICE CREAM...

SO THE UNIVERSE WAS REFILLED BY ... ROBOT TROUSER TRUMPS?

TRUMP!

AND SO THE UNIVERSE IS SAFE AGAIN...

AND IT'S ALL THANKS TO ROBOT ONE'S METAL BOTTOM!

UM, I THINK I NEED THE LOO...

I... I CAN TASTE BEANS...

THE END!

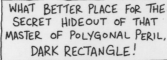

WHAT BETTER PLACE FOR THE SECRET HIDEOUT OF THAT MASTER OF POLYGONAL PERIL, DARK RECTANGLE!

DEATH PLANET, DEADLIEST PLANET IN THE UNIVERSE...

DEATH PLANET

KEEP OUT

NO JUNK MAIL

SIGH.

WHAT'S THE MATTER, MY RECTILINEAR REGENT? YOU DON'T SEEM TO BE YOUR USUAL VILLAINOUS SELF TODAY.

JUST LOOK AT IT, MURKY HEXAGON!

EVIL PLAN

VILLAINOUS PLOTS

DASTARDLY SCHEMES

SHOPPING LIST

DOESN'T IT MAKE YOU SICK?

UM, I DON'T SEE ANYTHING, OH PLANAR POTENTATE.

THE UNIVERSE, YOU SIX-SIDED SIMPLETON!

OHH, THE UNIVERSE.

I HATE EVERYTHING IN IT: STARS, PLANETS, MOUNTAINS, ROCKS, JELLYFISH, EVERYTHING!

AND DON'T EVEN GET ME STARTED ON PAPERCLIPS!

WHICH IS WHY I'M GOING TO DESTROY IT, WITH MY NEW UNIVERSE BOMB!

DESTROY THE UNIVERSE? BUT THAT'S WHERE I KEEP ALL MY THINGS!

CRACKLE!

U.B. 1000™

TO DO

THERE'S JUST ONE MORE THING I NEED TO COMPLETE MY PLAN...

... A NUBCHICK.

NUB CHICK
NUBBUSADORABILIS

MEANWHILE, IN SPACE...

WHAT'S A NUBCHICK?

THEY'RE THE UNIVERSE'S CUTEST, YET MOST ENDANGERED SPECIES, AND IT'S OUR MISSION TO TRANSPORT THE LAST FIVE SURVIVING SPECIMENS TO THE SPACE ZOO.

OOH, SO CUTE!

UBTUZ.

NUB! NUB! NUB! NUB! NUB NUB!

FAH! CUTENESS IS SUCH A PRIMITIVE CONCEPT! WE ROBOTS ARE FAR TOO ADVANCED TO BE CONCERNED ABOUT "ADORABILITY", AND WE ARE COMPLETELY UNABLE TO FEEL THIS EMOTION YOU CALL "OOGLY SNOOGLY".

OOH! NUB NUB NUB NUB HUG

THEN WHY ARE YOU WEARING A T-SHIRT THAT SAYS "I LOVE NUBCHICKS", ROBOT ONE?

OH, THIS? I WAS, UH, FEELING COLD...

I ♥ NUBCHICKS

BUT, CAPTAIN, HOW CAN SOMETHING SO ADORABLE BE SO ENDANGERED?

BECAUSE, PLIXX, AS WELL AS BEING THE UNIVERSE'S CUTEST SPECIES THEY ARE ALSO THE STUPIDEST.

NUB NUB NUB

SPACE LITTER

WHICH IS WHY WE HAVE TO KEEP A VERY CLOSE EYE ON THESE LAST FIVE NUBCHICKS...

NUB

NUUB

SPACE BLENDER

NUB!

SPACE TOASTER

ER, I MEAN, THESE LAST FOUR NUBCHICKS...

WHIRRR! FLOMP

CLICK

SPACE BLENDER

SPACE TOASTER

NUB?

NUB NUB

SO IT WOULD PROBABLY ALSO BE A GOOD IDEA IF YOU DIDN'T TRY TO EAT THEM, PILOT.

UVFTEBZ.

EXACTLY. NOW SET A COURSE FOR THE SPACE ZOO!

NUB

MEANWHILE, ON DEATH PLANET...

ALARM! ALARM! ALARM!

WHAT'S THAT, MY RHOMBOID RAJAH?

THAT'S MY NUBCHICK DETECTOR! THERE ARE NUBCHICKS NEARBY!

ACTIVATE THE VIEW-O-SCOPE!

NUBCHICK DETECTOR

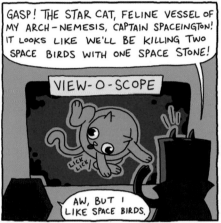

GASP! THE STAR CAT, FELINE VESSEL OF MY ARCH-NEMESIS, CAPTAIN SPACEINGTON! IT LOOKS LIKE WE'LL BE KILLING TWO SPACE BIRDS WITH ONE SPACE STONE!

VIEW-O-SCOPE

LICK LICK

AW, BUT I LIKE SPACE BIRDS.

ACTIVATE THE LASER!

WHIRR! CLUNK!

ABOARD THE STAR CAT...

CAPTAIN! CAPTAIN! EMERGENCY!

UM, CAPTAIN, WHY ARE YOU DRESSING UP THE NUBCHICKS IN LITTLE OUTFITS?

HOW MANY TIMES DO I HAVE TO TELL YOU TO KNOCK BEFORE YOU COME IN HERE, PLIXX?

NOW, WHAT IS IT?

NUB

POUR!

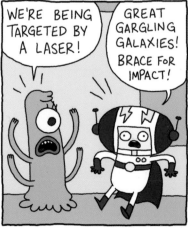

WE'RE BEING TARGETED BY A LASER!

GREAT GARGLING GALAXIES! BRACE FOR IMPACT!

FIRE!

BUT, CAPTAIN, I DON'T HAVE ANY BRACES...

BRAZEEM!

13

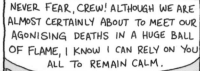
NEVER FEAR, CREW! ALTHOUGH WE ARE ALMOST CERTAINLY ABOUT TO MEET OUR AGONISING DEATHS IN A HUGE BALL OF FLAME, I KNOW I CAN RELY ON YOU ALL TO REMAIN CALM.

ACTIVATING PROGRAM PANIC.EXE: AAAAAAAH!

MUMMY!

BRAZEEEEEE
BING?

THAT'S IT? HA HA! THEY'LL HAVE TO DO A LOT BETTER THAN THAT TO BEST CAPTAIN SPACEINGTON!

SWISH

WELL, DANGER'S OVER – WHO FANCIES A CUPPA?

WARNING! SHINY OBJECT DETECTED!

UM, SIR...

POUNCE!

I FEEL DIZZY IN MY TUMMY!

UB.

AAAH!

PEER

WELL THAT WASN'T SO BAD...

BING
SWISH!

CRASH!

OOH, MY BRAIN HURTS!

EW, I THINK THAT MIGHT BE BECAUSE I LANDED ON IT...

SQUISH

WELL, WE MIGHT HAVE CRASHED, BUT AT LEAST IT'S OVER...

...WE'RE SAFE NOW.

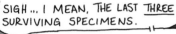
WELCOME TO DEATH PLANET

SHORTLY...

OK, CREW, WHILE THE PILOT IS REPAIRING THE STAR CAT IT'S IMPORTANT THAT WE KEEP THE NUBCHICKS SECURE.

WHACK WHACK

WHATEVER HAPPENS, WE MUST NOT LET THE LAST FOUR SURVIVING SPECIMENS OUT OF OUR SIGHT.

UM, SIR...

SIGH... I MEAN, THE LAST THREE SURVIVING SPECIMENS.

NOW, THIS COULD BE A VERY DANGEROUS PLANET, SO WHATEVER YOU DO, DON'T TOUCH ANYTHING.

CRUNCH

OH... SO YOU THINK MAYBE I SHOULDN'T HAVE PULLED THIS LEVER THEN...?

PROBABLY NOT, PLIXX...

TRAP DOOR

AAAAH!

AAAAH!

AAAAH!

NUB NUB!

CLUNK!

WEE! CAN I GO BACK UP AND RIDE AGAIN?

UGH, WHERE ARE WE? I CAN'T SEE A THING...

ACTIVATING PAIN SUBROUTINE:
10 PRINT "OW"
20 GOTO 10

LET ME ACTIVATE MY NIGHT VISION VISOR...

PRESS!

SHOONK

OH NO! THEY'RE ALL AROUND US! THERE'S SO MANY OF THEM! WE'RE DOOMED! WE'RE...

...

PLIXX, HAVE YOU BEEN EATING JELLY OUT OF MY HELMET AGAIN?

IT KEEPS IT FRESH!

OK, THERE'S OBVIOUSLY NOTHING DOWN HERE, LET'S GO...

UM, CAPTAIN?...

BOK

OOH, A STRANGE ALIEN LIFE-FORM! AS SPACE EXPLORERS IT'S OUR DUTY TO STUDY IT!

EW, IT'S ALL SLIMY AND ONLY HAS ONE EYE - DISGUSTING!

BOK

DON'T WORRY, PLIXX, IT'S JUST ONE HARMLESS ALIEN.

BOK

UM...

BOK

BOK

BOK

...AND I THINK THE BEST PLACE TO STUDY THEM WOULD BE FROM BEHIND THIS ROCK...

BAH!

YOU ORGANIC LIFE-FORMS ARE SO COWARDLY! WE ROBOTS ARE NOT FRIGHTENED OF ANYTHING!

SKREEEEEE!

...

BOK!

AFTER FURTHER ANALYSIS, I'VE CALCULATED THAT, ACTUALLY, IT WOULD BE BETTER TO STAY BEHIND THE ROCK.

PLIXX, WE NEED MORE INFORMATION ABOUT THE ALIEN. ACTIVATE YOUR SCANNER!

OK, SIR!

BLIP! BEEP!

SKREEE!

HMM, THIS IS VERY INTERESTING...

POKE PRESS FIDDLE

YOU'RE PLAYING A VIDEO GAME, AREN'T YOU?

SHH! I'M ON THE LAST BOSS!

SKREEEEE!

HEY! I ALMOST HAD A HIGH SCORE!

SLAP!

QUICKLY! EVERYONE IN THE CAVE! THE ALIEN'S TOO BIG TO FOLLOW!

SKREEE!

WAIT, I SEE LIGHT AT THE END OF THE TUNNEL— MAYBE IT'S A WAY OUT!

PLIXX, GRAB THE NUBCHICKS AND WE CAN GET OUT OF HERE!

THE NUBCHICKS? I THOUGHT ROBOT ONE HAD THEM?

MY DATABANKS INDICATE THAT I THOUGHT THE CAPTAIN HAD THEM...

WELL THEN, WHO HAS THEM?

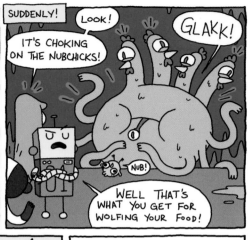

QUICKLY, PILOT, GET US OUT OF HERE!

HRRK! HRRKK!

UM, ARE YOU OK?

GREAT GLOBULES OF GLISTENING GALAXIES! A NUBCHICK! I'VE NEVER BEEN SO HAPPY TO SEE THE PILOT REGURGITATE!

RALP!

N-NUB

SPLUT

WELL IT LOOKS LIKE EVERYTHING'S TURNED OUT OK — WE ESCAPED DARK RECTANGLE, SAVED THE UNIVERSE, AND STILL HAVE ONE NUBCHICK TO TAKE TO THE ZOO!

YOU KNOW, I CAN SEE WHY DARK RECTANGLE LIKED THESE THINGS SO MUCH — THEY REALLY ARE ADORABLE.

PAT PAT

RRRRR...

?

GRAAAA!

AAAAH!

IT'S GONE BERSERK!

RAAA!

GET IT OFF!

GET IT OFF!

AAAAH!

RAAAAAA

DANGER! AIRLOCK

FLING!

KICK!

RAAAAAA AAAAA

DANGER! AIRLOCK

SLAM!

AIRLOCK RELEASE

UM, SIR, YOU JUST BLASTED THE UNIVERSE'S LAST SURVIVING NUBCHICK INTO SPACE... WHAT ARE WE GOING TO TELL THE SPACE ZOO...?

UM...

AND SO...

WELCOME TO THE SPACE ZOO

NUB.

NUB.

UM, WHAT WAS MY LINE AGAIN?

PLEASE DO NOT FEED THE NUBCHICKS

WAAAA!

THE END

THE HORROR OF MECHA DRACULA

WE JOIN THE CREW AT A MOMENT OF GREAT IMPORTANCE: THE FIRST VISIT TO A STRANGE NEW PLANET...

I HEREBY WELCOME PIZZA PLANET TO THE FEDERATION OF ALLIED REPUBLICS AND TERRITORIES

WE WELCOME THESE PEPPERONI SLICES AS TASTY NEW CITIZENS OF THE FEDERATION AND PLEDGE TO PROTECT THEIR WORLD FROM ALL...

UM, WHAT HAPPENED TO THIS BIT OF THE PLANET?

WE'RE JUST, UM, TAKING A MINERAL SAMPLE...

SUDDENLY!

HRK!

UM, ARE YOU OK? IF THIS IS GOING TO BE LIKE THE TIME WE VISITED CANDY FLOSS PLANET I'LL GET A BUCKET...

CAPTAIN SPACEINGTON! I'M CONTACTING YOU VIA ROBOT ONE'S EMERGENCY COMMUNICATOR FOR AN URGENT MISSION!

SPACE MAYOR! WHAT IS IT?

GLK!

POP!

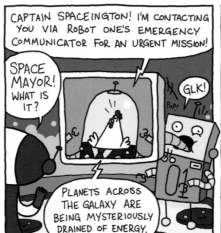

PLANETS ACROSS THE GALAXY ARE BEING MYSTERIOUSLY DRAINED OF ENERGY.

DRAINED OF ENERGY? HOW?

WE JUST DON'T KNOW!

OUR ONLY CLUE IS TWO STRANGE HOLES FOUND IN THE SURFACE OF EVERY PLANET...

SHRIVELLED

HOLE

DRAINED

MYSTERIOUS

GROSS

DON'T WORRY, SIR, WE'LL SOLVE THIS MYSTERY!

SCIENCE OFFICER PLIXX, WHAT DO YOU MAKE OF IT?

HMM...

ENERGY DRAINED...

STRANGE HOLES...

THINK THINK

SCRIT SCRIT

THERE'S ONLY ONE THING IT COULD BE...

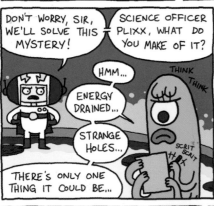

SPACE PIXIES!

THEY USE THE ENERGY TO RUN THE GIGGLE GENERATORS!

SPACE PIXIES

FOR THE LAST TIME, PLIXX, THERE'S NO SUCH THING AS SPACE PIXIES.

OH YEAH? WELL THEN HOW DO YOU EXPLAIN HOW MY CHOCOLATE PUDDINGS KEEP DISAPPEARING?

GLAAAA

ROBOT ONE, BRING UP THE GALACTIC MAP...

GLK!

OK, WE'RE HERE... NOW, CONNECT UP ALL THE PLANETS THAT HAVE BEEN AFFECTED-MAYBE WE'LL BE ABLE TO SEE A PATTERN.

HMM...

NO, THERE'S NO CLUE WHERE THE NEXT ATTACK WILL BE...

I GUESS THIS IS ONE PUZZLE THAT MAY NEVER BE SOLVED...

UM...SIR?

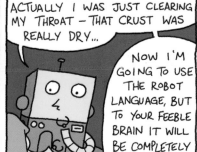

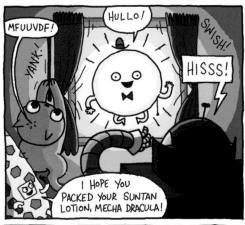

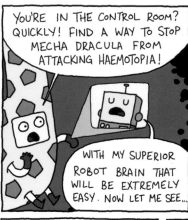

YOU'RE IN THE CONTROL ROOM? QUICKLY! FIND A WAY TO STOP MECHA DRACULA FROM ATTACKING HAEMOTOPIA!

WITH MY SUPERIOR ROBOT BRAIN THAT WILL BE EXTREMELY EASY. NOW LET ME SEE...

HMM, PERHAPS THIS IS IT?

LASER EYES

PRESS!

DRINK BLOOD

MONSTER MASH

YIKES!

NECK SPLODE

I'M NOT SURE THAT WAS THE RIGHT BUTTON, ROBOT ONE...

WELL, HOW AM I SUPPOSED TO CONCENTRATE WITH YOU SCREAMING IN TERROR ALL THE TIME?

LEAN!

OOPS!

CLUNK!

BLOOD   ICECREAM

MEANWHILE...

BLOOD BLOOD BLOOD BLOOD BLOOD BLOOD BLOOD BLOOD BLOOD BLOOD

AAAAH!

BLOOD BLOOD BL... ICE CREAM!

DINGLE DINGLE DINGLE DING

SPACE ICE CREAM

WHY DO I SUDDENLY HAVE A VERY BAD FEELING?

SLURRRRPPP!

SPACE ICE CR...

I SHOULD HAVE BEEN A GREENGROCER!

ERROR! BRAIN FREEZE!

FROZEN!

YOU DID IT, ROBOT ONE!

I DID? ER, I MEAN, OF COURSE I DID! NOW I'LL SIMPLY CLIMB OUT OF THE TOP ESCAPE HATCH.

I THINK I MAY HAVE TAKEN A WRONG TURN.

WELL, MECHA DRACULA IS FROZEN, AND THE UNIVERSE IS SAVED. LET'S HEAD BACK TO THE STAR CAT TO CELEBRATE!

GONE

UM, DIDN'T WE PARK THE STAR CAT OVER THERE?

GIGGLE

QFBOVU CVUUFS!

HEE HEE

LA LA!

THE END

UM...

I THINK I MIGHT HAVE GOT A BIT CONFUSED...

GROAN.

DON'T WORRY, SIR! I CAN GET THROUGH THE LASERS AND TURN THEM OFF FROM THE OTHER SIDE!

YOU CAN?

STRETCHH!

SEE—THE LASERS DIDN'T EVEN TOUCH ME!

SPLODGE!

...

WELL, MAYBE THEY TOUCHED ME A TINY BIT...

SPLAT

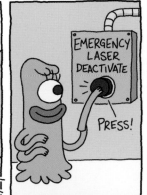

EMERGENCY LASER DEACTIVATE

PRESS!

GOOD WORK, PLIXX. NOW WHERE'S THE MOONA?

I GAVE IT TO THAT NICE ROBOT TO HOLD WHILE I JUMPED THROUGH THE LASERS.

NICE ROBOT?

ROB-OT!

EXIT

QUICKLY! I'LL USE THE MASTER CONTROL TO ACTIVATE A LOCK-DOWN AND STOP HIM ESCAPING!

UM...

?

...WHERE'S THE MASTER CONTROL?

NOT THERE!

OOH, HE'S GOOD...

PRESS

LASER ACTIVATE

THIS HAS NOT BEEN ONE OF MY BETTER DAYS...

CAN WE GO TO THE GIFT SHOP AFTER THIS?

ZUMMM!

GOOD WORK GETTING US OUT OF THERE, PLIXX!

NOW HOPEFULLY ROB-OT HASN'T STOLEN TOO MUCH WHILE WE WERE TRAPPED...

HALL OF EXTREMELY PRICELESS ART

NABBED! GONE! NICKED! STOLEN! PINCHED! FILCHED! HALF-INCHED! PLUNDERED!

ULP...

HELLO, CAPTAIN! HOW ARE THE SECURITY PREPARATIONS COMING ALONG?

GAH!

UH, FINE, YOUR CURATORLINESS...

EXCELLENT, EXCELLENT! NOW I REALLY MUST SHOW YOU SOME OF THE WONDERFUL SCULPTURES WE HAVE IN THIS ROOM...

PSST! QUICKLY CREW, ACTIVATE ACTION PROTOCOL ALPHA-14!

THIS PIECE REPRESENTS LOST LOVE — ISN'T IT BEAUTIFUL?

UM, ABSOLUTELY.

OH, BUT THE FOUNTAIN ISN'T WORKING... LET ME TAKE A CLOSER LOOK...

PSST! PLIXX!

AH, THAT'S MORE LIKE IT. ABSOLUTELY MAGICAL!

BLAAAA

YES, UH, SUBLIME

WELL, I'D BETTER LEAVE YOU TO IT — WE WOULDN'T WANT TO ALLOW ANY THIEVES IN HERE!

HA HA, NO!

PSST! CAPTAIN, LOOK! IT'S ROB-OT!

GASP!

ART DETECTED! ROB MODE ACTIVATED!

WE HAVE TO STOP HIM! WE JUST NEED SOME SORT OF BRILLIANT PLAN...

ROB

PRESS

DON'T WORRY, SIR, ALL I HAVE TO DO IS ACTIVATE MY BRILLIANT PLAN MODE AND I'LL HAVE A BRILLIANT PLAN FOR YOU IN SECONDS!

COO!

BRILLIANT PLAN MODE ACTIVATED! GENERATING BRILLIANT PLAN

1% COMPLETE

PRESS

SOME TIME LATER...

GENERATING BRILLIANT PLAN

4% COMPLETE

UM, I'LL GO AND CHECK THE GIFT SHOP FOR, ER, CLUES WHILE WE WAIT...

TAP TAP

EVENTUALLY...

BRILLIANT PLAN GENERATION COMPLETE!

100%

WOULD YOU LIKE TO VIEW THE PLAN Y/N?

EXCELLENT! WHAT IS IT?

I'M GOING TO BLOW ROB-OT UP WITH THIS BOMB.

BRILLIANT!

SOMEHOW THIS PLAN ISN'T QUITE AS BRILLIANT AS I HAD HOPED...

SPACE BOMB

SO... COME HERE AND LET ME BLOW YOU UP!

SPACE BOMB 01

PURSUE!

HELLO, CAPTAIN! THE ART EXPERTS HAVE JUST ARRIVED FOR THE EXHIBITION! I TRUST ALL IS WELL?

GULP! CURATOR!

ART ART ART A

UM, YES EVERYTHING IS TOTALLY PERFECT...

LOOK, THEY SELL TANKS OF FORMALDEHYDE IN THE GIFT SHOP SO YOU CAN MAKE YOUR OWN MODERN ART!

PLIXX! WATCH OUT!

SPACE BOMB

GIFT SHOP

ZOOM!

TRUNDLE TRUNDLE

OOF!

WHACK!

SPLOOSH!

MY FORMALDEHYDE!

GOODNESS ME, THIS IS A CHALLENGING NEW PIECE!

THIS COULD BE THE GREATEST ARTWORK OF A GENERATION!

THE ANGUISH OF CONFLICT, FROZEN IN TIME!

SPACE BOMB

ART DETECTED!

ART ART ART

SCREEEEEECH!

ROB MODE ACTIVATED!

GASP! ROB-OT!

WAIT, IS THIS PART OF THE ARTWORK?

SWIPE!

SPACE BOMB

I THINK THE ROBOT REPRESENTS THE FUTILITY OF MAN.

PAH! TOO DERIVATIVE.

?

BLOIK!

ART-SPLODE!

OOH! ALL THE ART IS BACK! BUT WHERE'S THE MOONA LISA?

WAIT, I THINK I SEE IT STILL IN HERE...

BURP!

RIPPPPP!

OH NO! WHAT WILL WE DO NOW?

WELL, THE CURATOR DID SAY NO ONE HAD SEEN IT BEFORE...

SO...

SIMPLY MAGNIFICENT!

THE EXPRESSION IS SO ENIGMATIC!

RESPLENDENT!

PSST! CAPTAIN, I THINK YOU'RE A HIT!

THE END

TURNIP in TIME

AS OUR THRILLING STORY BEGINS, THE STAR CAT IS DOCKED AT SCIENCE STATION ALPHA...

THANK YOU FOR COMING TO HELP WITH MY EXPERIMENT, CAPTAIN SPACEINGTON.

WE'RE ALWAYS HAPPY TO HELP IN THE FURTHERANCE OF SCIENCE, PROFESSOR NEMATOCYST.

OH YES, I'M AN EXPERT IN ALL THE SCIENCES!

PERHAPS MY SCIENCE OFFICER COULD BE OF SOME ASSISTANCE?

FIDDLE!

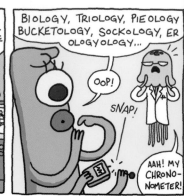

BIOLOGY, TRIOLOGY, PIEOLOGY BUCKETOLOGY, SOCKOLOGY, ER OLOGYOLOGY...

OOP!

SNAP!

AAH! MY CHRONO-NOMETER!

ON SECOND THOUGHTS, MAYBE YOU SHOULD JUST GET US SOME REFRESHMENTS, PLIXX.

SHOVE!

OOH, CAKE-OLOGY!

SO WHAT IS THIS EXPERIMENT ANYWAY?

WITH THE HELP OF THE STAR CAT'S SYSTEMS WE'RE FINALLY GOING TO PIERCE THE UNIVERSE'S FINAL BARRIER...

OFF

ON

OOH! YOU MEAN WE WILL FINALLY CROSS-BREED A RADISH AND A HEDGEHOG?

UM, NO... WE WILL TRAVEL THROUGH TIME ITSELF!

01

BEHOLD, SCIENCE'S GREATEST ACHIEVEMENT: THE TIME TURNIP!

CLONK

OOH! SWIRLY!

HMF, I'D RATHER HAVE A RADISH-HOG.

LOOK, I MADE SCIENCE CAKE! OOH, IS THAT A PARSNIP?

SCIENS IS GRATE

SQUEE SQUEE

OOPS!

PLIXX! WATCH OUT!

FLING!

SCIENS IS GRATE

TRIPP!

MY CAKE!

ZOT!

IT'S FALLEN INTO THE TURNIP TIME TUNNEL!

DON'T WORRY, LITTLE SPONGE. I'LL SAVE YOU!

WAIT, PLIXX, IT'S NOT WORTH IT!

LEAP!

YES IT WASN'T EVEN A CHOCOLATE CAKE!

GASP! SHE'S GONE! WILL PLIXX BE ALL RIGHT, PROFESSOR?

ZOT!

I'M AFRAID THE JOURNEY THROUGH TIME WILL BE UNIMAGINABLY TERRIFYING WE CAN'T BEGIN TO CONTEMPLATE THE HORRORS THAT YOUR CREW MEMBER WILL EXPERIENCE!

WEEEEEEEEE!

ONE MINUTE EARLIER...

LOOK, I MADE SCIENCE CAKE! OOH, IS THAT A SWEDE?

SQUEE SQUEE

SUDDENLY...

AGAIN!

ZOT!

SPLAT!

GASP!

TWO PLIXXES?! WHAT'S GOING ON?

CAPTAIN! I HAVE TRAVELLED FROM THE DISTANT FUTURE TO PREVENT A TERRIBLE ACCIDENT.

GREAT TRUMPETING TIME WARPS! WHAT IS IT?

AN ASTEROID? A SUPER NOVA? SPACE HAMSTERS??

WORSE THAN ALL OF THOSE: I'M GOING TO DROP THE CAKE!

NO! NOT THE CAKE!

YOU TRAVELLED THROUGH TIME TO SAVE A CAKE?

WELL, IT DOES HAVE STRAWBERRY ICING...

DON'T WORRY THOUGH, SIR, I KNOW JUST HOW TO FIX IT.

ALL I HAVE TO DO IS MOVE THIS DUCT OUT OF THE WAY SO I DON'T TRIP OVER IT...

UM, I'M NOT SURE YOU SHOULD PULL ON THAT...

OOPS!

EMISSION INTAKE

CAUTION!

POP!

YANK!

SCIENS IS GRATE

AAAH!

SUCKKKK!

THE CAKE!

EMMISSION INTAKE

IT'S BEEN SUCKED INTO THE STAR CAT'S EMISSION PROCESSING SYSTEM...

DON'T WORRY, CAPTAIN, MY ADVANCED ROBOTIC BRAIN HAS CALCULATED THAT THE CAKE WILL SIMPLY PASS HARMLESSLY THROUGH.

BLOIK!

CAKE-SPLODE

...

OPTUSJMT.

WELL, THAT DIDN'T GO ENTIRELY AS I PLANNED...

I KNOW! WE DIDN'T EVEN SAVE THE CAKE!

HMM, I THINK WE'RE GOING TO NEED MORE ASPIRIN.

CAPTAIN, CAN YOU TELL ME WHERE IT HURTS?

SIZZLE

...AND MAYBE A PLASTER.

OOPS.

FLOP

CLONK

DON'T WORRY CAPTAIN, I'LL PUT THIS RIGHT!

I'LL SEE YOU GUYS LATER! UM, I MEAN EARLIER... I THINK...

HEE HEE, WE'RE MAKING THEM KISS!

SMOOOCH! SMOOOCH!

HOP!

ZOT!

ONE MINUTE EARLIER...

STOP PULLING!

NO, YOU STOP PULLING!

STOP!

I HAVE TRAVELLED FROM THE DISTANT FUTURE TO PREVENT A TERRIBLE ACCIDENT!

OOH!

SCIENCE IS GUMS

ZOT!

ANOTHER TERRIBLE ACCIDENT? WHAT... SAY, THAT SKULL LOOKS KIND OF FAMILIAR.

GULP!

UM, IT'S NOTHING FOR YOU TO WORRY ABOUT, CAPTAIN IT'S JUST A TEENY-TINY TERRIBLE ACCIDENT...

...AND ALL I HAVE TO DO IS TURN THIS OFF AND EVERY-THING WILL BE OK!

CLUNK

HIDE!

AAH! WHAT ARE YOU DOING? THAT'S THE TEMPORAL STABILISER! WITHOUT THAT THE TIME TUNNEL WILL TEAR THE UNIVERSE APART!

TURN IT BACK ON!

OOPS!

SNAP

DOES ANYONE HAVE ANY STICKY TAPE?

SWIRLL!

AAAAAAAAAAAAAAAAH!

PPPP

RRRR

BGGBCME.

WELL, IT SEEMS LIKE PLIXX HAS DESTROYED THE UNIVERSE...

SO, UM, THERE'S NOT, REALLY MUCH TO SEE.

SORRY.

OH, IT LOOKS LIKE PLIXX IS STILL HERE...

OOPS.

PLIXX!

OOH, WHO'S THAT?

WHAT HAVE YOU DONE WITH THE UNIVERSE, PLIXX?

OH!

I KNOW IT WAS HERE A MINUTE AGO.

WELL, UM, THERE WAS THIS CAKE, SEE, AND...

WAIT, WAS IT A CHOCOLATE CAKE?

WELL, NO BUT...

SILENCE!

DO YOU HAVE ANY IDEA HOW LONG IT TOOK ME TO MAKE THAT UNIVERSE??

I MEAN, JUST MAKING ONE ANT TAKES AGES, AND THERE WERE, LIKE MILLIONS OF THEM.

AND DON'T EVEN GET ME STARTED ON HOW LONG IT TAKES TO MAKE AN OWL.

BUILD YOUR OWN ANT KIT

WHAT DO YOU HAVE TO SAY FOR YOURSELF??

I... I... I'M REALLY, REALLY, REALLY SORRY!

AND?

AND I PROMISE NEVER TO DESTROY THE UNIVERSE EVER AGAIN!

HMM, LOOK, I'M NOT REALLY SUPPOSED TO DO THIS, BUT I REALLY DON'T WANT TO HAVE TO START ALL OVER AGAIN.

I'M GOING TO GIVE YOU ONE MORE CHANCE.

OH, THANK YOU!

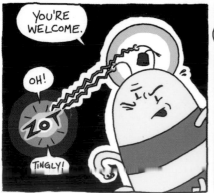

YOU'RE WELCOME.

OH!

ZO

TINGLY!

SIGH.

THIS WOULD NEVER HAVE HAPPENED IF I'D MADE EVERY- THING OUT OF ICE CREAM LIKE I WANTED TO...

OH WELL, NEXT TIME...

ONE MINUTE EARLIER...

I'M HERE TO STOP A TERRIBLE ACCIDENT!

NO, I AM!

YOU'RE ALL WRONG, I HAVE TO DO IT!

DOES ANYONE WANT SOME CAKE?

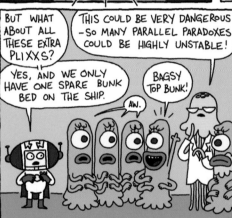

THE THINGY

As our adventure begins the crew is taking on vital provisions...

GOOD NEWS, CAPTAIN, THE NEW TEAPOT HAS ARRIVED!

EXCELLENT!

JUST TRY NOT TO ACCIDENTALLY SWALLOW THIS ONE.

CAPTAIN SPACEINGTON! THIS IS A LEVEL 11 SPACE ALERT! A DANGEROUS SPACE CRIMINAL HAS ESCAPED FROM SPACE JAIL AND IS ON THE LOOSE IN YOUR SECTOR! (OF SPACE!)

SPACE MAYOR! FEAR NOT, MY CREW EATS SPACE CRIMINALS FOR SPACE BREAKFAST!

BZZT!

WITH MINI MARSHMALLOWS!

THIS IS NO ORDINARY CRIMINAL, CAPTAIN - IT'S A SHAPE-SHIFTER, ABLE TO PERFECTLY COPY ANY OBJECT OR PERSON! YOU MUST BE ON HIGHEST ALERT FOR ANYTHING SUSPICIOUS — THAT CREATURE MUST NOT BE ALLOWED TO GET ON BOARD THE SHIP!

DON'T WORRY, YOUR MAYORNESS, I SHALL BE AS VIGILANT AS VIGILOR, THE 117-EYED VIGILANCE-BOT OF THE PLANET VIGILAX IV.

WHICH IS TO SAY, VERY, VERY VIGILANT.

UM, CAPTAIN, THE DELIVERY MAN DISAPPEARED, AND NOW THERE ARE TWO TEAPOTS...

PLIXX, CAN'T YOU SEE I'M TALKING TO THE MAYOR? JUST BRING THEM BOTH ABOARD AND STOP BOTHERING ME!

SORRY ABOUT THAT, YOUR MAYOROSITY — WAS THERE ANYTHING ELSE?

I DID HAVE ONE QUESTION...

IS THAT A TEAPOT CLIMBING UP YOUR WALL?

AAH! IT'S THE SHAPE-SHIFTER! AND IT'S GOING FOR THE LIGHT SWITCH!

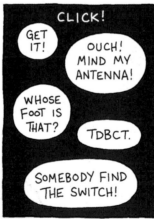

CLICK!

GET IT!

OUCH! MIND MY ANTENNA!

WHOSE FOOT IS THAT?

TDBCT.

SOMEBODY FIND THE SWITCH!

IT'S GONE!

OR MAYBE IT'S DISGUISED AS SOMETHING ELSE IN THE ROOM...

CLICK!

OR MAYBE IT'S DISGUISED...

...AS ONE OF US.

NOW, EVERYBODY STAY CALM — WE MUSTN'T TURN AGAINST EACH OTHER...

HA! THAT'S EXACTLY WHAT A SHAPE-SHIFTER WOULD SAY!

BSNBEJMMP.

THAT IS ALSO EXACTLY WHAT A SHAPE-SHIFTER WOULD SAY!

THIS ISN'T GETTING US ANYWHERE. ROBOT ONE, ACCESS YOUR DATABASE OF ALIEN LIFE-FORMS AND SEE IF YOU CAN FIND OUT ANYTHING ABOUT SHAPE-SHIFTERS.

UM, OK, ACCESSING DATABASE...

HMM, ACCORDING TO THIS, SHAPE-SHIFTERS CAN BE UNIQUELY IDENTIFIED BY A SEVERE ALLERGY TO SAUCEPANS...

MY FIRST BOOK OF ALIENS

SO IT'S PROBABLY NOT A GOOD IDEA TO ASK ONE TO DO THE WASHING UP.

SAUCEPANS? I DON'T SEE HOW THAT WILL HELP US TO...

?

OW! HEY!

A-HA! SEE THAT? IT HURT HIM! HE MUST BE THE SHAPE-SHIFTER!

CLONK

GIVE ME THAT! I'LL SHOW YOU WHO'S ALLERGIC TO SAUCE-PANS...

SNATCH!

WEE!

OW!

CLONK

PLIXX, STOP THAT! HITTING PEOPLE WITH PANS ISN'T GOING TO HELP US FIND THE IMPOSTER!

OH, I'D FORGOTTEN ALL ABOUT THE IMPOSTER - I JUST LIKE THAT 'CLONK' SOUND.

THIS IS HOPE-LESS! WE'RE NEVER GOING TO WORK OUT WHICH OF US IS THE SHAPE-SHIFTER!

WAIT, MAYBE IT'S THAT GIANT BLUE CHICKEN THAT'S BEEN STANDING IN THE CORNER SINCE THE LIGHTS CAME BACK ON?

AW, HOW DID YOU GUESS?

IT'S RUNNING INTO THE STORAGE BAY! PLIXX AND I WILL FOLLOW IT, YOU TWO STAY HERE IN CASE IT DOUBLES BACK.

STORAGE

BOKAWK!

ANY QUESTIONS?

CLONK

JUST CHECKING. YOU CAN GO NOW...

ALL RIGHT, PLIXX, WE'VE GOT IT TRAPPED. LET'S GO!

EXIT

SPACE OIL

THERE'S NOWHERE LEFT TO RUN, VILLAIN! QUICKLY PLIXX! THE PAN!

GULP!

...ER, PLIXX?

UM, I'M HAVING SOME MINOR TECHNICAL DIFFICULTIES WITH THE APPARATUS, CAPTAIN.

WHERE'S THE UNDO BUTTON?

I SEE YOU FOUND THE SHAPE-SHIFTER.

CAN'T YOU? ONLY A COMPLETE IDIOT WOULDN'T BE ABLE TO SEE IT!

YOU CAN TELL THEM APART?

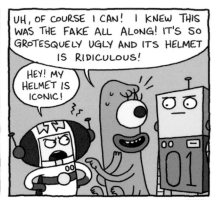

UH, OF COURSE I CAN! I KNEW THIS WAS THE FAKE ALL ALONG! IT'S SO GROTESQUELY UGLY AND ITS HELMET IS RIDICULOUS!

HEY! MY HELMET IS ICONIC!

LOOK, THERE'S ONE WAY TO SETTLE THIS FOR SURE:

CAPTAIN, CAN WE STAY UP ALL NIGHT PLAYING VIDEO GAMES?

WHAT? ABSOLUTELY NOT! THAT'S IN CLEAR VIOLATION OF SENSIBLE BED-TIME DIRECTIVE #78142!

YESSSS! LET US PLAY THESE "VIDEO GAMES"! I AM THE CAPTAIN.

WELL THIS IS OBVIOUSLY THE REAL CAPTAIN – NOW, SHALL WE GO TO THE GAMES ROOM?

WOO! MY DECEPTION WAS A SUCCESS! UH, I MEAN, YES, LET US DO THAT.

SO... COME ON, YOU DIED AGAIN! LET ME HAVE A GO!

NO WAY! I DIED BECAUSE OF A BUG! THAT MEANS I GET A FREE GO!

COME ON, CAPTAIN SHARING IS FUN!

BIP BEEP BLOOP!

NO SHARING!

DID YOU SEE THAT? THIS IS TERR-IBLE...DOESN'T THE CAPTAIN KNOW; SHARING IS THE MOST POWERFUL FORCE IN THE UNIVERSE?

OK, I'LL TAKE CARE OF THIS...

ALL RIGHT, IMPOSTER, THE GAME IS UP: WE KNEW YOU WERE A FAKE ALL ALONG! WHAT DO YOU HAVE TO SAY ABOUT THAT?

OR IS IT GRAVITY? I ALWAYS GET THOSE TWO MIXED UP.

JUST ONE THING...

RAAAAAAAAAAAAAA!

AAAAAAAAAH!

OH, HANG ON, LET ME JUST SAVE MY GAME...

OH YES, YOU JUST GOT PAST A DIFFICULT BIT.

NOW, WHERE WAS I? OH YES... RAAAAAAAA!

AAAAAAAAH!

RAAAAA!

SORRY WE THOUGHT YOU WERE THE SHAPE-SHIFTER, CAPTAIN! BUT YOU HAVE TO HELP US!

THIS IS EXTREMELY DISAGREE-ABLE!

QUICKLY! USE THE SAUCEPANS! THEY'RE ITS ONLY WEAKNESS!

UNTIE!

UM, THE OTHER CAPTAIN ORDERED US TO THROW ALL THE SAUCEPANS OUT OF THE AIRLOCK.

WHICH IN RETROSPECT DOES SEEM A LITTLE SUSPICIOUS...

HMM, DON'T WORRY, I HAVE ANOTHER EVEN MORE BRILLIANT PLAN...

HEY! YOU'RE THE WORST SHAPE-SHIFTER I'VE EVER MET! I'VE KNOWN SPACE POTATOES BETTER AT DISGUISE THAN YOU!

WHAT? HEY! NO WAY, I'M THE BEST SHAPE-SHIFTER! I CAN TURN INTO ANYTHING!

OH YEAH? WELL I BET YOU COULDN'T TURN INTO...

...A PICKLE!

WINK!

NUDGE

HAVE YOU GOT SOMETHING IN YOUR EYE, CAPTAIN?

HA! THAT IS, LIKE, THE EASIEST THING YOU COULD HAVE ASKED ME TO TURN INTO! WATCH THIS!

SHIFT! CHANGE!

TA-DA!

BLORP!

HA, YOU FELL INTO MY TRAP! NOW, QUICKLY, CREW EAT THE VILLAIN!

NOW, STEADY ON!

ER...

...I DON'T REALLY LIKE PICKLES...

YEAH, THEY'RE ALL SLIMY AND GROSS...

FINE, IF YOU WANT SOMETHING EATEN PROPERLY, YOU HAVE TO EAT IT YOURSELF!

GULP!

THERE'S NO ESCAPE NOW, YOU NEBULOUS NE'ER-DO-WELL!

AAAH!

BONK!

PQQT.

SLORP!

OI! WATCH IT!

JUMBO JAR O' PICKLES

TRIP!

AAH! HOW AM I GOING TO FIND THE RIGHT PICKLE NOW??

PICKLY AROMA

THERE'S ONLY ONE THING FOR IT...

...I'M GOING TO HAVE TO EAT THEM ALL!

GLOM! CHOMP!

GRAB!

30 MINUTES LATER...

BLEH... THIS IS THE LAST PICKLE... MUST EAT IT TO BE SURE... BUT I DON'T THINK I CAN EAT EVEN ONE MORE...

BLOIK

I CAN EAT IT IF YOU LIKE? I LOVE PICKLES!

YOU! BUT I THOUGHT YOU WERE A PICKLE!

OH, I CHANGED BACK A WHILE AGO, BUT YOU WERE ENJOYING THOSE PICKLES SO MUCH I DIDN'T WANT TO DISTURB YOU.

SPLAP!

ENOUGH OF THESE GAMES, YOU FORMLESS FIEND! GET OFF MY SHIP!

CAN'T I STAY? PLEEASE?

AW, BUT I JUST WANTED TO BE FRIENDS! IT'S SO LONELY BEING A SHAPE-SHIFTER

HMM... I DON'T KNOW...

HOW ABOUT WE PUT IT TO A VOTE - IF THE CREW WANTS ME TO LEAVE I'LL GO WITHOUT A FIGHT.

I SUPPOSE THAT SOUNDS FAIR - ALL THOSE THAT WANT THE SHAPE-SHIFTER TO STAY, RAISE YOUR HANDS.

WELL, IT LOOKS LIKE IT'S UNANIMOUS! I GUESS THAT MEANS YOU CAN...

SAY, WAIT A MINUTE...

DEMOCRACY!

THAT'S EXTREMELY UNDEMOCRATIC! NO MORE CHANCES - GET OFF MY SHIP!

SHOVE!

COME ON! I'LL DO ANYTHING IF YOU LET ME STAY!

NOTHING YOU CAN DO WILL CONVINCE US TO LET YOU STAY!

I COULD... BAKE A CAKE?

WELCOME ABOARD!

GLAD TO HAVE YOU ON THE CREW!

BAGSY I GET TO LICK THE BOWL.

AW!

SO...

OK, ALL I NEED NOW IS SOMETHING TO MELT THE BUTTER IN...

BQPTUSPQIF.

THANK YOU.

SAY, IS THIS A SAUCEPAN?

MY ALLERGIES!

SWELL

BLOAT!

BLOOSH!!

...

ON SECOND THOUGHTS, YOU CAN LICK THE BOWL, PLIXX.

YAYY!

THE END

39

INCORPOREAL PUNISHMENT

CAPTAIN! I'M PICKING UP A STRANGE ENERGY READING!

THAT MUST BE WHAT WE CAME FOR... WHERE'S IT COMING FROM?

WELL, IT SEEMS LIKE IT'S COMING FROM...

BIP BIP BIP BIP BIP BIP

...ON BOARD THE SHIP!

GASP! THERE MUST BE AN INTRUDER ON BOARD! QUICKLY! FIND THE SOURCE!

AS OUR STORY BEGINS, THE STAR CAT IS ON A MISSION IN A DISTANT GALAXY TO INVESTIGATE A MYSTERIOUS ENERGY SIGNATURE...

IT'S COMING FROM INSIDE THIS CUPBOARD...

GULP, OK, LET'S OPEN IT ON THE COUNT OF 3. 1... 2...

...3!

GASP!

PLIXX, THIS IS A PORCUPINE.

WAIT A MINUTE, THIS ISN'T AN ENERGY DETECTOR, IT'S A RODENT DETECTOR! I MUST HAVE GOT THEM MIXED UP.

CRONCH CRONCH

CRISPS

WHICH EXPLAINS WHY I COULDN'T FIND MY CAPYBARA YESTERDAY.

WELL THIS WAS A COMPLETE WASTE OF TIME, PLOT A COURSE FOR HOME!

HUGS! OW!

HUGS! OW!

CAPTAIN! THE CONTROLS AREN'T RESPONDING! SOMETHING'S STOPPING THE SHIP FROM MOVING!

WAGGLE

NOPE NUH-UH

TAK TAK

ALLITERATIVE ASSERTIONS! WHAT INCREDIBLE FORCE COULD HOLD AN ENTIRE SHIP IN PLACE? WHAT INCONCEIVABLE TECHNOLOGY COULD HAVE SUCH POWER?

IT APPEARS TO BE A VERY LARGE CARD-BOARD BOX, SIR.

OUR GREATEST WEAKNESS! THIS MUST BE RELATED TO THE STRANGE ENERGY SOURCE.

BUT WHAT COULD IT BE?

HA HA HA HA HA HA! PUNY MORTALS! YOU CANNOT HOPE TO UNDERSTAND!

THAT VOICE! WHERE'S IT COMING FROM? SHOW YOURSELF!

VERY WELL, FOOLISH CREATURE, I WILL SHOW MYSELF, BUT KNOW THIS: I AM A BEING OF PURE ENERGY FROM BEYOND TIME AND SPACE AS YOU KNOW IT; MY TRUE FORM IS BEYOND ALL COMPREHENSION TO YOUR PRIMITIVE MINDS AND GAZING UPON IT WILL LIKELY DRIVE YOU ALL _MAD_! NOW, BEHOLD...

OOER...

...MY TRUE FORM!

MANIFEST!

...

IS ANYONE GOING MAD YET?

SO WHAT ARE YOU? LIKE, A GHOST OR SOMETHING?

I AM A COSMIC ENTITY! ALL-KNOWING! ALL-POWERFUL!

EVERY ATOM IN THE UNIVERSE BENDS TO MY WILL!

UM, YOUR SHOELACE IS UNTIED.

UH, I MEANT THAT, OBVIOUSLY...

SUCH IS MY WILL!

NOW, DOES THE RABBIT GO DOWN THE HOLE OR ROUND THE TREE...?

TIE TIE

SO, UM, DO YOU HAVE A NAME?

MY NAME EXISTS IN 17 DIMENSIONS AT ONCE - IF I WERE TO SPEAK IT IN THIS UNIVERSE IT COULD DESTROY HALF THE GALAXY!

COULD YOU WRITE IT DOWN?

OK!

SKRIT SKRIT

BEHOLD THE INCOMPREHENSIBLE WONDER OF MY TRUE NAME!

DO NOT ATTEMPT TO UNDERSTAND IT, FOR TO PRONOUNCE EVEN THE FIRST HALF OF THE FIRST SYLLABLE WOULD BE ENOUGH TO DESTROY THIS SHIP AND EVERYONE ON BOARD!

YOUR NAME IS ... ALLEN?

AAAH!

WHAT HAVE YOU DONE? WE'RE DOOMED! WE'RE...

HUH, WELL, I MUST BE THINKING OF SOME OTHER UNIVERSE...

?

ENOUGH OF THIS! WHY ARE YOU HOLDING US IN YOUR DIABOLICAL SNARE?

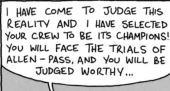

I HAVE COME TO JUDGE THIS REALITY AND I HAVE SELECTED YOUR CREW TO BE ITS CHAMPIONS! YOU WILL FACE THE TRIALS OF ALLEN - PASS, AND YOU WILL BE JUDGED WORTHY...

OOH, WILL THERE BE PRIZES?

BUT IF YOU FAIL...

...I WILL ERASE YOUR ENTIRE PATHETIC UNIVERSE FROM EXISTENCE, LIKE A BOTTLE OF TIPP-EX SPILLED ACROSS YOUR MATHS HOMEWORK!

SPLAM!

YOU CAN'T FORCE MY CREW TO PLAY YOUR GAMES, YOU INCORPOREAL INTERLOPER!

GET HIM!

RUNNING APPLICATION GRAB_ALLEN.EXE

THE APPLICATION HAS ENCOUNTERED AN ERROR! SUBMIT A BUG REPORT? Y/N

HA! PUNY MORTALS! YOU ARE NO MATCH FOR ME!

GRAB!

POOF!

TELEPORT!

WE'LL SEE ABOUT THAT!

SEE HOW I BEND REALITY TO MY WILL TO EVADE YOUR ATTACKS WITH EASE!

GASP!

S-T-R-E-T-C-H

ZOW!

BSUJDIPLFT.

EVEN YOUR WEAPONS ARE UNDER MY COMMAND!

WAK..

ZOINK

YOU ARE HELPLESS!

AS YOU SEE, I CAN PREDICT YOUR EVERY MOVE — YOU MAY AS WELL GIVE UP N—

SMUG!

WAK!

MY BREADBOX!

DUCK-ASSAULT!

SWIIISH!

PXM.

THAT... THAT DOESN'T COUNT... I WASN'T ... READY ... OOF.

VERY WELL, IT SEEMS WE HAVE NO CHOICE — WE'LL FACE YOUR TRIALS.

EXCELLENT! THEN I SHALL TRANSPORT US TO THE ARENA OF TRIALS WITH MY INCREDIBLE COSMIC POWERS!

COSMIIIC

POWERRRRS

OO-ER!

SPLING!

YOU KNOW, THIS ARENA OF TRIALS LOOKS A LOT LIKE THE INSIDE OF OUR BROOM CUPBOARD...

UM, YES ...THAT WAS THE FIRST TRIAL- THE TRIAL OF BROOM CUPBOARDS! CONGRATULATIONS: YOU PASSED!

NOW, UH, LET'S TRY THAT AGAIN...

SPLING!

BEHOLD! THE ARENA OF TRIALS!

HEY! WHAT HAPPENED TO OUR CLOTHES?

YOU ARE DRESSED FOR YOUR FIRST TRIAL - THE TRIAL OF COURAGE!

SPLING!

I CAN'T SEE!

I HAVE SEARCHED YOUR ENTIRE UNIVERSE FOR IT'S MOST FEARED CREATURE, A BEAST THAT STRIKES TERROR INTO WHOLE GALAXIES, AND SEALED IT BEHIND THIS GATE...

LEVER!

CLANK CLANK CLANK

NOW TO SAVE YOUR UNIVERSE YOU MUST FACE THIS MONSTER IN COMBAT, LET THE TERROR BEGIN!

FLIT FLIT

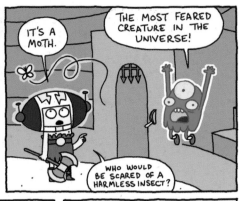

IT'S A MOTH.

THE MOST FEARED CREATURE IN THE UNIVERSE!

WHO WOULD BE SCARED OF A HARMLESS INSECT?

AAAH! GET IT AWAY! GET IT AWAY!

IT'S COMING RIGHT FOR MY FACE! AAAAAH!

THERE'S NOTHING TO BE AFRAID OF, IT'S JUST A MOTH!

SEE HOW YOUR COURAGEOUS CAPTAIN DEFEATS THE CREATURE WITH EASE.

COWER!

WAAAA! IT'S TOUCHING MY FACE WITH ITS PAPERY WINGS! THE HORROR! THE HORROR!

D-DID ANYONE SEE WHERE IT WENT?

LAND!

IT'S ON MY HEAD! GET IT! GET IT!

OK, OK, JUST HOLD STILL...

FLIT FLIT

THUNK

OUCH!

OOPS.

AAAH! NOW IT'S COMING FOR ME! IT'S AFTER BLOOD!

AAH! FLIT

DID YOU GET IT?

SWISHH!

UM, NOT QUITE...

AAAAH!

YOU KNOW, THIS TRIAL ISN'T REALLY GOING THAT WELL SO FAR...

FLIT FLIT

43

AAAAAH!

OH.

POUNCE!

DVUJDMFT.

SPLAP!

FLIT

FLIT

CONGRATULATIONS! YOU HAVE PASSED THE TEST OF COURAGE! I AM MOST IMPRESSED!

CRUNCH CRUNCH

ALSO, KIND OF GROSSED-OUT.

NOW FOR THE NEXT TEST: THE TRIAL OF MIND, WHERE YOUR INTELLIGENCE SHALL BE TESTED TO ITS VERY LIMIT!

DON'T WORRY, CAPTAIN, I CAN HANDLE THIS.

MY ADVANCED ROBOTIC MIND IS 18,000 TIMES MORE POWERFUL THAN THAT LUMP OF GREASY MUSH YOU LAUGHABLY CALL A BRAIN.

YOU DO REALISE YOU STILL HAVE AN AXE IN YOUR HEAD, RIGHT?

OHH — I WONDERED WHY MY HELMET DIDN'T FIT.

VERY WELL, YOUR CHAMPION IS CHOSEN. NOW FACE THE MIND-BOGGLING CONUNDRUM OF...

HARD SUMS

THE MATHS HOMEWORK!

MATHS HOMEWORK...?

GET EVEN ONE SUM WRONG AND YOUR UNIVERSE IS DOOMED.

DOOMED!

HA! EASY SQUEEZY! MY BRAIN IS LIKE A CALCULATOR! YOU KNOW, ONE OF THOSE FANCY ONES WITH ALL THE FUNNY SYMBOLS.

THIS BOOK BELONGS TO ALLEN

THE TRIAL BEGINS!

MATHS MATHS

AND CONTINUES!

LET'S SEE...

CARRY THE FOUR...

MORE MATHS!

EVENTUALLY!

FINISHED!

ARE YOU QUITE SURE? EVEN THE TINIEST MISTAKE WILL SPELL THE END FOR ALL EXISTENCE.

YEAH, YEAH, FINAL ANSWER.

OK, LET THE MARKING COMMENCE!

THIS BOOK BELONGS TO ALLEN

HARD SUMS

UM, FOR THE QUESTION "WHAT IS 4+4" HE'S PUT "12ISH"... I'M NOT SURE THAT'S RIGHT...

EH, CLOSE ENOUGH, YOU HAVE PASSED THE TRIAL!

WOO! RO-BOT ONE! RO-BOT ONE!

TOSS!

COSMIC SHRUG

NOW FOR THE NEXT TRIAL!

...THE TRIAL OF WASHING UP!

WASHING UP? YOU KNOW, I EXPECTED THESE TRIALS TO BE A LITTLE MORE... INTERESTING.

OH REALLY? WELL PERHAPS YOU'LL THINK AGAIN WHEN I TELL YOU...

...THE FOOD IS BURNED ON.

NOOOOO!

SUPER CRUSTY

YOU'RE GOING STRAIGHT TO SPACE JAIL, DARK RECTANGLE!

BUT LOOK, I HAVE A "GET OUT OF SPACE JAIL FREE" CARD, SO I GET ANOTHER GO!

NO!

SHAKE SHAKE

I CAN BEAR THIS CORRUPT SYSTEM NO LONGER!

HEY! JUST BECAUSE I HAD A HOTEL ON SPACE MAYFAIR!

FLIP!

I CAN'T BELIEVE MY CREW LEFT ME TO FOLLOW THAT STUPID STARBLAZE.

HEY! STARBLAZE IS THE COOLEST!

SPACE SULK

I BET THEY'RE REGRETTING IT ALREADY!

MEANWHILE, ON THE STARCAT...

...AND THAT'S HOW I BEAT THE LAVA DOLPHINS OF PORPOISION 7.

SO COOL!

OOH, NOW TELL US HOW YOU BEAT THE LASER SLUGS OF MUCOSIA 5.

IF ONLY I KNEW WHAT THE MISSION WAS THEN I COULD GO AND DO IT, AND SHOW THEM THAT I'M THE BEST CAPTAIN...

MAYBE WE CAN ACCESS STARBLAZE'S EMAIL FROM THE COMPUTER IN THE SPACE FALCON, MY MANY DIMENSIONAL MASTER.

HEY, STOP HELPING THE GOOD GUYS!

EXCELLENT IDEA, PLIXX! UH, I MEAN, MURKY HEXAGON.

TRACTOR!

KREEE!

I'LL BRING THE WRECKAGE IN WITH THE TRACTOR BEAM...

SHORTLY...

OK, I THINK I FOUND HIS PERSONAL FILES...

OOH! DOES HE SAY ANYTHING ABOUT ME?

THAT'S NOT WHAT WE'RE SUPPOSED TO BE LOOKING FOR!

KREEE..?

ALTHOUGH MAYBE JUST CHECK AND SEE IF THERE'S ANYTHING ABOUT ME ON THERE...

ACTUALLY IT'S ENCRYPTED — IT WILL TAKE ME A WHILE TO BREAK THE CODE...

BAH! IS THERE ANYTHING TO DO AROUND HERE WHILE WE WAIT?

OOH! I KNOW A SUPER-FUN GAME!

BONG BONG BONG

LET'S USE ONE OF MY DOOMSDAY DEVICES TO DESTROY THE UNIVERSE!

THIS ONE SEALS STARS INSIDE GIANT POTATOES TO CREATE AN ETERNAL NIGHT AND A TASTY BAKED TREAT!

THIS ONE WILL DESTROY THE LETTER "R" PLUNGING THE UNIVERSE INTO A NEW EIGN OF TEO AND FEA!

AND THIS ONE ... UM, ACTUALLY I'M NOT SURE WHAT THIS ONE DOES...

SPROING

MAYBE I SHOULD JUST TURN IT ON...

OH NO YOU DON'T! WE'RE NOT ACTIVATING ANY OF THESE DEVICES!

HEY!

BLOOMP!

OOPS.

ACTIVATE /PRESS!

SNATCH!

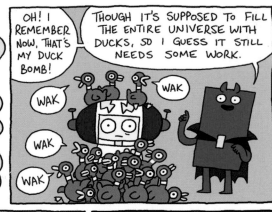

OH! I REMEMBER NOW, THAT'S MY DUCK BOMB!

THOUGH IT'S SUPPOSED TO FILL THE ENTIRE UNIVERSE WITH DUCKS, SO I GUESS IT STILL NEEDS SOME WORK.

WAK

WAK

WAK

WAK

WHAT IS IT WITH YOU AND DESTROYING THE UNIVERSE ANYWAY?

A GUY'S GOT TO HAVE A HOBBY — NOW WHERE DID I PUT THAT HYPER-BOMB?

WAK

↑ HYPER BOMB

I'VE PARTIALLY DECODED THE FILES, OH NON-POLYGONAL PALADIN, BUT THEY'RE STILL NOT COMPLETELY CORRECT...

JUST LET ME SEE WHAT YOU HAVE SO FAR.

GASP!

SECRET MISSION

TUESDAY 14TH OF SPACE JUNE

TODAY I WILL HAVE A SURPRISE ATTACK FOR SPACE MAYOR. HE WILL BE TOTALLY DESTROYED WHEN I GIVE HIM A HUGE BOMB!

SO STARBLAZE DIDN'T GET AN EMAIL FROM THE SPACE MAYOR AT ALL...?

THIS MEANS STAR-BLAZE IS... A VILLAIN??

THIS IS BRILLIANT! NOW I CAN BE THE BRAVEST CAPTAIN!

UH...

UM, I MEAN, THIS IS AWFUL AND WE HAVE TO STOP HIM.

WHAT DO YOU MEAN WE? I'M A VILLAIN TOO, REMEMBER?

IF STARBLAZE WANTS TO BLOW UP SPACE HQ WITH A HUGE BOMB JUST LIKE THE ONE THAT'S GONE MISSING FROM MY COLLECTION THEN I DON'T SEE WHY I WOULD...

WAIT! MY HYPER-BOMB! HE'S PINCHED IT! NO ONE STEALS MY BOMBS!

QUICKLY, TO THE POLYGON MOBILE!

WHAT ARE YOU WAITING FOR, SPACEINGTON — ARE YOU COMING OR NOT?

SLOT!

UM, THE DOOR IS JUST A SLOT — I DON'T THINK I CAN...

COME ON, YOU JUST NEED A LITTLE PUSH!

OW OW OW! I DON'T THINK THIS IS GOING TO WORK!

PUSH!

PULL!

SIGH, ALL RIGHT, FATTY, I HAVE A BETTER IDEA...

AND SO...

AAAAAAAH!

IS HE GOING TO MAKE THAT NOISE FOR THE WHOLE JOURNEY?

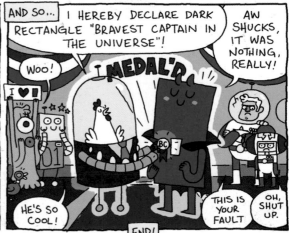

NOTHING TO FEAR BUT FEAR ITSELF...

(BUT FEAR IS REALLY, REALLY SCARY)

AS OUR STORY BEGINS, THE STAR CAT IS IN ORBIT AROUND THE PLANET LATEXIA, PICKING UP A CONSIGNMENT OF SUPPLIES OF THE UTMOST IMPORTANCE...

WE'VE SUCCESSFULLY RECEIVED THE SHIPMENT OF RUBBER CHICKENS, SPACE MAYOR.

EXCELLENT WORK, CAPTAIN SPACEINGTON.

RUBBER CHICKENS

THE PLANET CLOWNTOPIA-8 IS SUFFERING ITS WORST RUBBER-CHICKEN FAMINE IN DECADES - IT'S VITAL THAT YOU DELIVER THIS SHIPMENT AS QUICKLY AS POSSIBLE, OR I DREAD TO THINK WHAT MIGHT HAPPEN.

YOU CAN COUNT ON US, SIR - THESE FLEXIBLE FOWL WILL BE THERE IN NO TIME.

PLIXX, PLOT A DIRECT COURSE FOR CLOWNTOPIA-8.

BUT, CAPTAIN, THAT COURSE WOULD TAKE US RIGHT THROUGH THE CENTRE OF...

...THE SPOOKY QUADRANT!

THE BISCUIT QUADRANT

THE SPOOKY QUADRANT
HERE BE SPOOKS!

LATEXIA
X
THE RABBIT QUADRANT

CLOWNTOPIA
X

THE SALTY QUADRANT

OOOOOOOOOO!

NO AMOUNT OF SPOOKINESS IS SPOOKY ENOUGH TO SPOOK IN OUR WAY - THOSE PEOPLE ARE COUNTING ON US FOR THESE AMUSING NOVELTY ITEMS AND WE CANNOT LET THEM DOWN!

PILOT, TAKE US IN!

WE MUST PROCEED WITH CAUTION, CREW: THIS SECTOR IS FILLED WITH HAZARDS... SPOOKY HAZARDS!

INKY PINKY DINKY

PLIXX, WHAT DATA DO WE HAVE ON THIS REGION?

OOH, THIS QUADRANT IS FULL OF SO MANY COOL THINGS! LOOK, THERE'S THE GHOST PLANET, THE GHOST OF A PLANET THAT DIED OF FRIGHT ... BECAUSE IT SAW A GHOST!

WOOOOO

A ROUGH GUIDE TO THE SPOOKY QUADRANT

BORING! I'VE SEEN SPOOKIER THINGS IN THE CAPTAIN'S BATHTUB.

01

...AND LOOK! THERE'S THE WERE-MOON, THAT TURNS INTO A TERRIFYING HALF-MAN, HALF-MOON CREATURE WHENEVER IT SEES A FULL WOLF!

TRANSFORM!

AWOOOO!

NOT AGAIN! SHOO!

MUMMY WORLD

WERE-MOON

UGH, MY TEDIUM CAPACITOR IS IN DANGER OF OVER LOADING.

...AND SPOOKIEST OF ALL, SPACE CASTLE SPACEFERATU - IT'S BEEN ABANDONED FOR HUNDREDS OF YEARS, BUT LEGEND SAYS THAT ITS CORRIDORS ARE PROWLED BY A TERRIBLE BLOOD-SUCKING FIEND!

SNORE-UNIT ACTIVATED! THERE IS CLEARLY NOTHING IN THIS WHOLE SECTOR THAT COULD EVEN SLIGHTLY STIMULATE MY INTEREST PROCESSOR...

 THERE'S NO NEED TO WASTE ANY MORE TIME HERE – PILOT, SET SPEED TO MAXIMUM AND GET US OUT OF...

CAPTAIN SPACEINGTON! CAPTAIN SPACEINGTON! COME IN!

COMMS

AN INCOMING TRANSMISSION FROM THE SPACE MAYOR!

UM, SOMETHING LOOKS A LITTLE DIFFERENT ABOUT YOU TODAY, YOUR MAYORLINESS...

I'VE, UH, HAD A HAIRCUT... BUT THAT'S NOT IMPORTANT RIGHT NOW. I WANT YOU PUNY ORGANIC BEINGS, UM, I MEAN, BRAVE SPACE PEOPLE TO INVESTIGATE CASTLE SPACEFERATU IMMEDIATELY.

IT'S VITAL THAT YOU FIND ALL THE TREASURE, ER, I MEAN, SCIENCE THAT IS THERE. NOW GET TO WORK!

WELL, ROBOT ONE, IT LOOKS LIKE YOU WERE RIGHT – WE'VE BEEN ORDERED TO...

BLIT!

?

SAY – WHERE IS ROBOT ONE?

OH, THERE YOU ARE... WHAT ARE YOU DOING?

NO TIME TO EXPLAIN, CAPTAIN, THERE ARE IMPORTANT SCIENCE THINGIES TO INVESTIGATE!

SPACE CAM

ATTACH!

MESSAGE COMPLETE

AND SO...

DOCKING COMPLETE, CAPTAIN! WE'RE READY TO BOARD.

AIR LOCK

I'M NOT SURE WE SHOULD BE LEAVING SUCH AN IMPORTANT SHIPMENT BEHIND...

NO NEED TO STIMULATE YOUR PRIMITIVE HUMAN WORRY-GLAND, CAPTAIN.

THE PILOT WILL BE HERE TO GUARD IT – WHAT COULD POSSIBLY GO WRONG?

I GUESS YOU'RE RIGHT...

101 RUBBER CHICKEN RECIPES

CAREFUL, CAPTAIN, MY SPOOKINESS DETECTOR INDICATES THAT THE SPOOKINESS LEVELS IN HERE ARE "SCREAMING HEEBIE-JEEBIES"!

YOU'RE RIGHT, PLIXX – WE'D BETTER STICK TOGETHER.

AIR LOCK

NOT WELCOME

OH WOW, LOOK AT ALL THIS TREASURE!

LET'S SHARE IT!

SHARING IS FUN!

NOOOOO!

HMM...

ACTUALLY, I'VE CALCULATED THAT WE SHOULD DEFINITELY SPLIT UP. NOTHING BAD EVER HAPPENS WHEN PEOPLE SPLIT UP.

HMM - I'M NOT SURE THAT'S SUCH A GOOD IDEA...

PLIXX, WHAT DO YOU THINK?

HELLO, PLIXX! I'M A TALKING APPLE!

YAAAAY!

HMM...

YAAAAY!

VERY WELL, IT LOOKS LIKE WE'RE AGREED - WE'LL SPLIT UP AND MEET BACK HERE IN AN HOUR.

YESSSS...

...THAT'S RIGHT, MY LITTLE KITTENS...

DIVIDE YOURSELVES AND COME DEEPER INTO MY LAIR...

...AND SOON THE SPACE VAMPYR SHALL FEED!

WU-HA-HA-HA-HA-HA!

OOH, ARE WE DOING SHADOW PUPPETS? LOOK, I CAN DO A RABBIT!

OOP!

...AND LOOK, THIS ONE'S A UNICORN RIDING A VELOCI-

HELLO...?

THAT'S FUNNY - I COULD HAVE SWORN THERE WAS A SHADOWY FIGURE, SINISTERLY FORESHADOWING OUR TERRIBLE FATES HERE A MOMENT AGO...

OH WELL, I MUST HAVE IMAGINED IT...

SSSS!

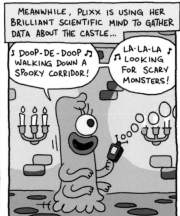

I SHALL RETURN!

PFOOF!

GONE!

I, UH, FORGOT MY KEYSSS...

SSORRY ABOUT THIS.

PFOOF!

I CAN'T EVEN FIND GOOD VILLAINS THESE DAYS...

PFOOF

GONE! AGAIN!

MEANWHILE...

DRAG FASTER, MINIONS!

I'M GOING TO BE FILTHY RICH! OR AT LEAST HEAVILY SOILED!

CRONCH CRONCH

AND BEST OF ALL, I'M DEFINITELY NOT BEING LURED INTO A TRAP BY MY SUPERIOR ROBOT GREED!

UGH, THIS ISN'T GOLD! IT'S...

... MATHS HOMEWORK?

PFOO

$4 + 7 = 18$
$8 + 2 = 148$

I SEE YOU FINALLY BROUGHT IN YOUR HOMEWORK, MR ONE!

ULP! THAT VOICE... IT CAN'T BE... IT'S...

GRAB!

NOW, LET ME GET MY MARKING LASER OUT...

MISS TEACHER-BOT! BUT I HAVEN'T SEEN HER SINCE...

WUMM

TB1000

...GULP... ROBOT SCHOOL!

HA HA HA HA HA HA HA HA HA HA HA HA HA HA HA HA HA HA HA

THIS IS JUST LIKE MY NIGHTMARES... BACK IN SCHOOL... IN TROUBLE WITH TEACHER... NAKED IN FRONT OF THE WHOLE CLASS...

OH WAIT, I'M ALWAYS NAKED...

THIS HOMEWORK IS TERRIBLE, ROBOT ONE!

ZAP

TB1000

WORST MARK IN THE CLASS AGAIN! WHY CAN'T YOU BE MORE LIKE THE OTHER STUDENTS?

I-I DON'T KNOW...

WE KNOW, MISS!

F

TB1000

IT'S BECAUSE HE'S...

YUM YUM! I'VE BEEN TRAPPED ALONE AND STARVING IN THIS CASTLE FOR MILLENNIA, BUT NOW YOU'RE HERE AS MY PRISONERS I'LL BE ABLE TO FEED ON YOU FOR CENTURIES!

YOUR VILLAINOUS SCHEME WON'T WORK, YOU PHOBO-PHAGIC FIEND! OUR LOYAL PILOT WILL HAVE NOTICED THAT WE ARE MISSING BY NOW, AND IS ALMOST CERTAINLY LAUNCHING A DARING RESCUE ATTEMPT AS WE SPEAK!

MEANWHILE, ON BOARD THE STAR CAT...

EBNNJU, KJN, J'N B EPDUPS, OPU B NJSBDMF XPSLFS!

CLICK CLICK

CHOM

CHOM

RUBBER CHICKENS

NO ONE IS COMING TO SAVE YOU, MY LITTLE CHIPMUNKS! I AM THE SPACE VAMPYR! I CAN TAKE ANY FORM AND SUBJECT YOU TO YOUR GREATEST FEARS...

BEHOLD!

CHANGE

SHIFT

TRANSFORM

I AM YOUR FEAR THAT IN A THOUSAND YEARS EVERYTHING YOU HAVE EVER DONE WILL BE FORGOTTEN, THAT EVERY ACTION YOU TAKE IS ULTIMATELY MEANINGLESS! WU HA HA HA HA!

UM...

I DON'T REALLY...

HMM, MAYBE THAT... ONE'S A BIT TOO HIGH-CONCEPT. OK, WHAT ABOUT IF I TURN INTO...

SCRATCH SCRATCH

SHRUG

...A BIG SPIDER! BOO!

TRANSFORM!

AAAAAA AAAAAA!

OH YUM, YOUR FEAR IS LIKE CHOCOLATE BISCUITS MIXED WITH BACON SANDWICHES, WE'RE GOING TO HAVE SO MUCH FUN!

FEARRRRRRR

RUB RUB

WE CAN'T LET THIS FEARSOME FIEND GET THE BETTER OF US, CREW! BE BRAVE!

REMEMBER: WE HAVE NOTHING TO FEAR BUT FEAR ITSELF!

WHAT ABOUT A BIG RAT?

OH MY STARS! AND RATS! AND RATS!

AAAAAA

61

OH, SORRY.

THAT'S BETTER.

AAAAAH!

THE HORROR!

AAAAAAAAAH!

NO! STOP IT! TOO MUCH FEAR! YOUR COWARDICE IS TOO STRONG!

SWELL

BLOAT

BLURP.

FEAR-SPLODE

WE DID IT! OUR PATHETIC LACK OF COURAGE SAVED THE DAY AGAIN! I'M SO PROUD OF YOU ALL!

I THINK I GOT SEMI-DIGESTED FEAR IN MY MOUTH...

IT'S BONE-CHILLINGLY DELICIOUS!

COME ON, LET'S GET BACK TO THE SHIP...

BACK ON THE STAR CAT...

PILOT, SET A COURSE FOR CLOWNTOPIA-8 — WE'VE ALREADY WASTED ENOUGH TIME AND IF WE DON'T GET THOSE RUBBER CHICKENS DELIVERED SOON I DREAD TO THINK WHAT MIGHT HAPPEN!

CPPLDBTF.

UGH, THAT WAS AWFUL. AND AFTER ALL THAT, THE GALACTIC OMNI-CROWN WASN'T EVEN REAL! I SHOULD HAVE JUST STAYED HERE WITH YOU, PILOT.

SAY, WHERE DID ALL THESE RUBBER CHICKEN BONES COME FROM...?

XBJTUDPBU.

UGH, I DON'T KNOW WHY I EVEN BOTHER. YOU REALLY HAVE ABSOLUTELY NO IDEA WHAT'S GOING ON, DO YOU?

FNQSFTT.

PLONK

THE END!

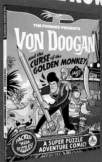